KT-556-473

Ace Logic Brainstumpers

LAGOON
BOOKS

1

Managing Editor: Simon Melhuish
Series Editor: Nikole G. Bamford
Contributors: Philip Carter
Design: Alan Shiner

Designed and compiled by
Lagoon Books
PO Box 311, KT2 5QW, UK
PO Box 990676, Boston, MA 02199, USA

ISBN: 1905439776

© Lagoon Books 2006
Lagoon Books is a trade mark of The Lagoon Trading Company Limited.
All rights reserved.

No part of this publication may be reproduced, stored in a retrieval system,
or transmitted in any form or by any other means electronic, mechanical,
photocopying or otherwise, without prior permission in writing from the publisher.

www.thelagoongroup.com

Printed in China

Ace Logic Brainstumpers

What number should replace the question mark?

A 2
B 4
C 3
D 1

4

Which ellipse should replace the question mark?

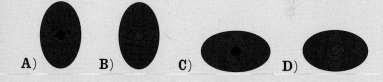

A)   B)   C)   D)

5

What comes next?

tare, aloud, poet, real, dupe, ?

A raft
B spill
C strap
D tree

Only one group of five letters below can be
rearranged to spell out a five-letter word
in the English language.

A APERM

B OUBRL

C EMNAP

D ATEIL

Can you identify the word?

7

Which pentagon should replace the question mark?

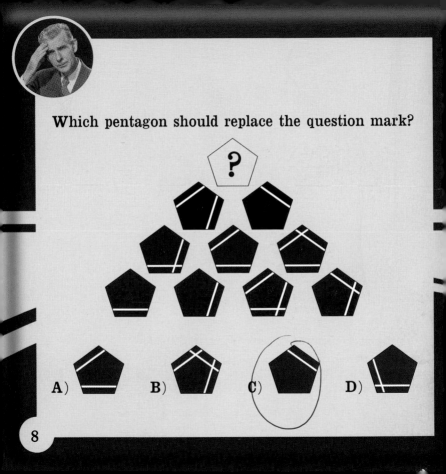

A)   B)   C)   D)

Which number should replace the question mark?

15   1

127   31

7   3

?

A   63
B   74
C   65
D   59

What number should replace the question mark?

6 3 19 5 7 ?

16 2 18 15

A 13
B 14
C 9
D 11

Which number should replace the question mark?

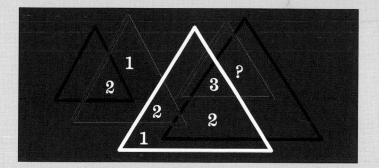

A 1
B 4
C 3
D 2

What point of the compass lies at
112.5 clockwise from north?

A ESE
B ESW
C SE
D SSE

What number should replace the question mark?

4	23	8
7	41	2
9	27	8
3	51	5
8	84	6
3	81	6
3	72	?

A 8
B 12
C 9
D 4

"That's a nice cup," said Danny.
"But it doesn't match the saucer," said Sally.
"It's because I bought them separately," said
David. "The cup cost $1 more than the saucer, and
the cost of them both added together cost $1.50."

How much did the saucer cost?
      A $0.50
      B $0.25
      C $0.60
      D $0.75

What two letters come next?

A Z B Y D W G T ? ?

A LO
B JQ
C KP
D KO

What comes next?

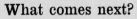

Z
X
U
Q
?

A L
B M
C K
D N

What letters are missing?

FIN ORA STE ISH

TOR ???

A ADY
B USE
C CAS
D ENT

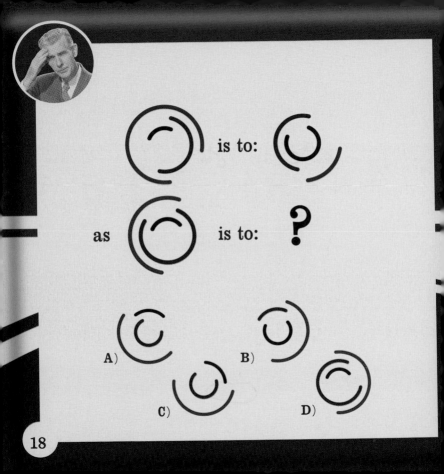

is to:

as ⬡ is to: **?**

A)

B)

C)

D)

What comes next?

tuneful
federal
refusal
?

A astound
B fuchsia
C success
D lantern

19

Find the starting point and work from letter
to adjacent letter horizontally and vertically,
but not diagonally, to spell out a twelve-letter word.

Which is the missing letter?

A   M
B   D
C   S
D   Q

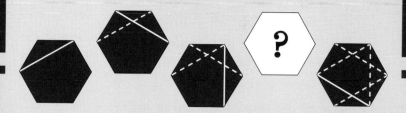

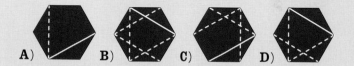

A)   B)   C)   D)

What letters are missing?

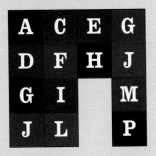

A	C	E	G
D	F	H	J
G	I		M
J	L		P

A)
K
M

B)
L
N

C)
J
K

D)
K
N

22

What comes next?

fabric
disbelief
nightlife
jackal
?

A alphabet
B abacus
C mentor
D sequence

23

What word is missing from the second column?

broke   rage

prose   cute

dared   evil

sung   ?

A men
B women
C people
D lasses

24

Which is the odd one out?

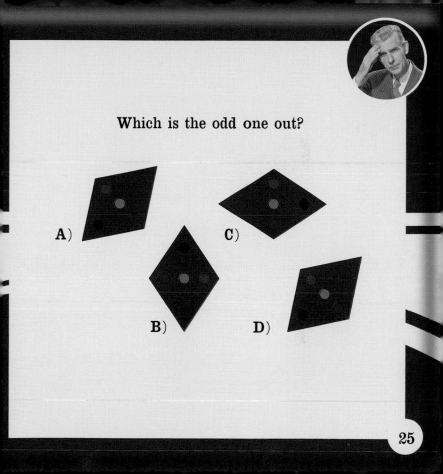

A)

C)

B)

D)

Only one group of five letters below can be rearranged to spell out a five-letter word in the English language.

A YENOL

B CIUTN

C NEFCI

D NUGAL

Can you identify the word?

Which is the odd one out?

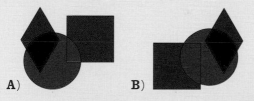

A)

B)

C)

D)

What number should replace the question mark?

VIEW = 11
TAXI = 8
LINE = 10
HALT = ?

A 12
B 14
C 10
D 8

Which of the following is an anagram of a
two word phrase that is pronounced
the same as the phrase below?

PEACE TALKS

A swept lake
B false pork
C stark poles
D speak last

How many lines are there below?

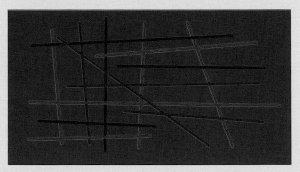

    A 12
    B 13
    C 14
    D 15

What weight should replace the question mark in order to balance the scales?

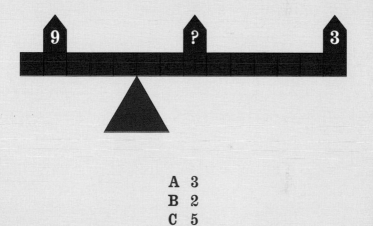

A 3
B 2
C 5
D 9

What letter is immediately to the right of the
letter that comes midway between the letter
immediately to the left of the letter C
and the letter immediately to the
right of the letter E?

$$\mathcal{A} \ \mathcal{B} \ \mathcal{C} \ \mathcal{D} \ \mathcal{E} \ \mathcal{F} \ \mathcal{G} \ \mathcal{H}$$

A	E
B	G
C	C
D	B

Which is the odd one out?

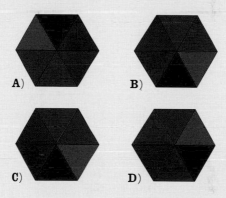

A)

B)

C)

D)

Which is the odd one out?

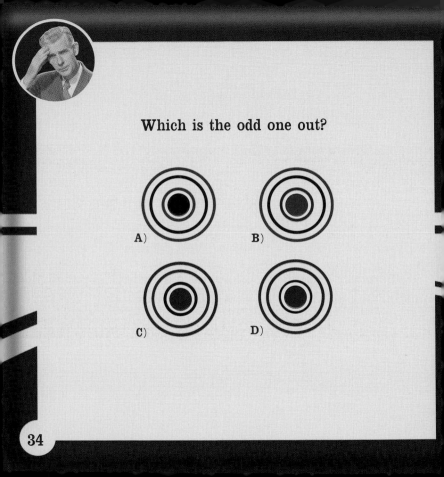

A)

B)

C)

D)

What comes next?

AB, DEF, HIJK, ?????

A OPQRS
B LMNOP
C NOPQR
D MNOPQ

What number should replace the question mark?

9	6	3	7
8	4	8	6
9	1	8	2
5	3	?	6

A 1
B 0
C 3
D 2

Three of the four strings of letters below can
be combined to spell out a phrase.
Which is the unused string?

A **tal**
B **goi**
C **ead**
D **one**

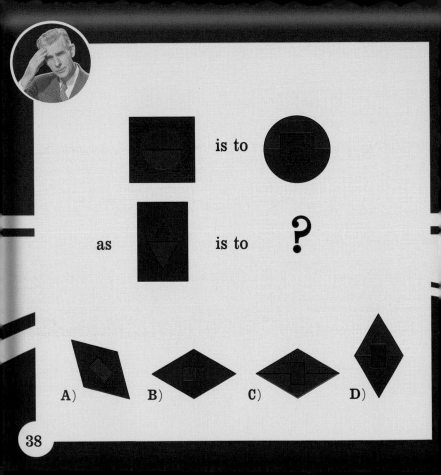

is to

as

is to

?

A) B) C) D)

38

What number should replace the question mark?

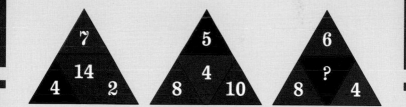

A 10
B 12
C 8
D 6

What shape should replace the question mark?

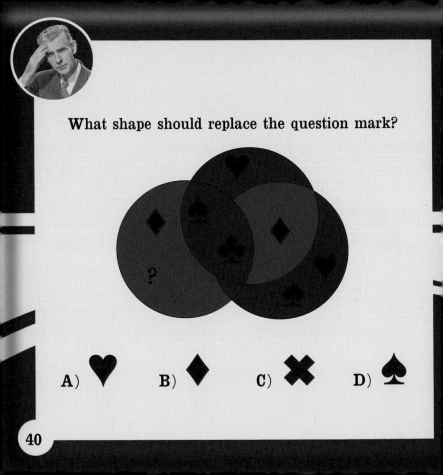

A) ♥   B) ♦   C) ✖   D) ♠

Which word in the right-hand column belongs in the left-hand column?

cap	trip
mare	break
owl	dream
	club

A trip
B club
C break
D dream

What day comes two days after the day that comes four days before the day that comes the day after the day that comes two days before Friday?

SUNDAY
MONDAY
TUESDAY
WEDNESDAY
THURSDAY
FRIDAY
SATURDAY

A   Friday
B   Tuesday
C   Wednesday
D   Thursday

Which is the odd one out?

A GHKJ
B LMON
C CDFE
D STVU

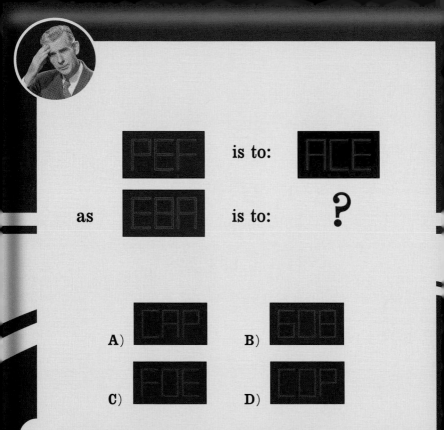

PEF is to: ACE

as EBA is to: ?

A) CAP

B) 8OB

C) FOE

D) COP

44

What number should replace the question mark?

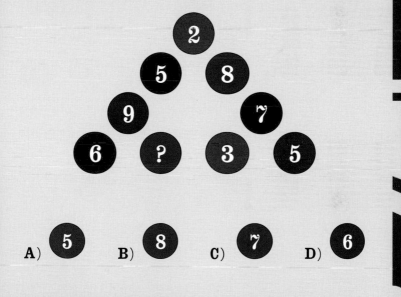

A) 5   B) 8   C) 7   D) 6

What letter is three letters to the right of the letter immediately to the left of the letter three letters to the right of the letter B?

$$\mathcal{A} \, \mathcal{B} \, \mathcal{C} \, \mathcal{D} \, \mathcal{E} \, \mathcal{F} \, \mathcal{G} \, \mathcal{H}$$

A	F
B	G
C	E
D	D

Which is the missing tile?

A)

B)

C)

D)

What letter is missing

P P U U L S L ?

A   L
B   S
C   H
D   E

A 6-letter word appears reading clockwise.

What is the missing letter?

A   U
B   A
C   E
D   I

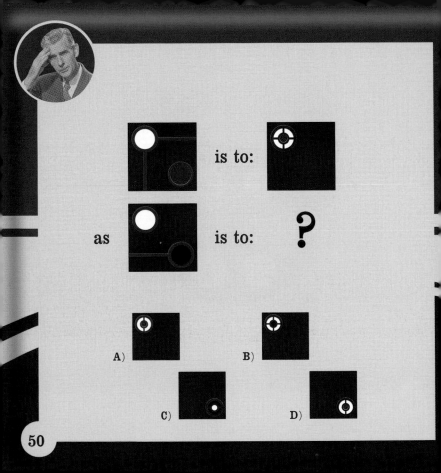

is to:

as   is to: ?

A)

B)

C)

D)

Which word below is most opposite in meaning to

Frangible?

A unsteady
B unbreakable
C unhelpful
D unbelievable

Which word is missing?

MISS MASS LASS **?** LADY

A LADS
B PASS
C LAST
D LOSS

Which word is missing?

ROUGH	ACHE
WORK	?

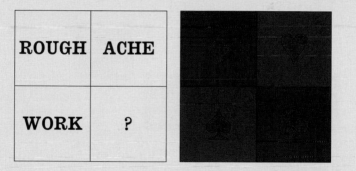

A fan
B mind
C hope
D tip

Below are the views of the top of five dice.

What is the total of the bottom faces of the five dice?

A 16
B 18
C 14
D 15

What is the value of DOG?

COW = 31523
PIG = 1697
RAT = 18120
DOG = ?

A 3826
B 4157
C 5157
D 3926

When the below is folded to form a cube, which is the only one of the following that can be produced?

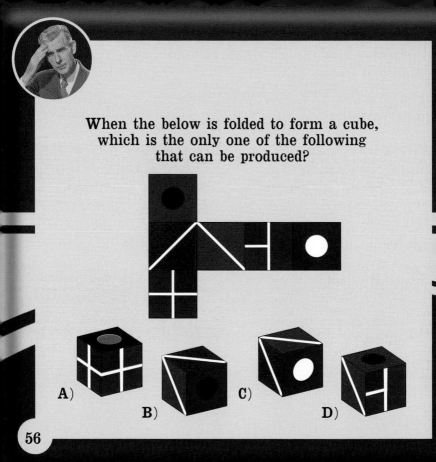

A)

B)

C)

D)

What letters are missing?

NR DR ?? FY MH AL

A ET
B EL
C JY
D JR

What letter can be inserted into the below several times to produce a sequence of related words?

ECHFXTRTGLFHTEL

A   I
B   A
C   O
D   U

What word completes the sequence below?

melodic, vehicle, eastern, mandate, juggler, saffron, urgency

?

A impulse
B pacific
C wayward
D nebular

What comes next?

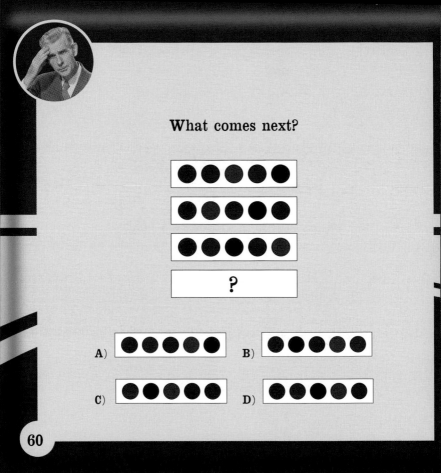

What letter can be removed from a word meaning

rank

to produce a word meaning

rate of speed?

A   L
B   G
C   E
D   T

Which is the odd one out?

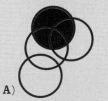

A)

B)

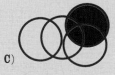

C)

D)

What is the difference between the average
of the numbers below and the
second highest odd number?

546987852

A 0
B 1
C 2
D 3

Which square should replace the question mark in the sequence below?

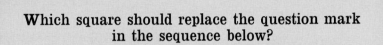

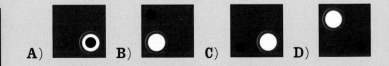

Three of the four pieces can be fitted
together to form a perfect square.
Which is the odd piece out?

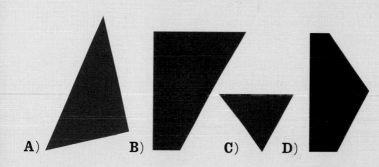

A)   B)   C)   D)

Which anagram below reveals a word
that will correctly complete the quotation
by Louis Pasteur?

Chance favors the
(_____) mind

A deep rap
B spar peer
C drop peers
D rapper Ed

What word is opposite in meaning to

Piquant?

A tart
B pleased
C slow
D bland

Which is the missing tile?

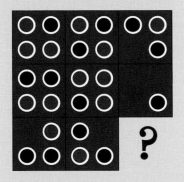

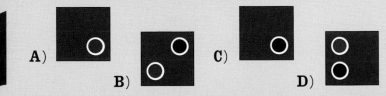

A)

B)

C)

D)

EJK

is to

HLO

as

PMT

is to

?

A RPW
B ROX
C SPW
D SOX

How many minutes is it before 12 noon
if six minutes ago it was twice as
many minutes past 11 am?

A 18 minutes
B 16 minutes
C 21 minutes
D 22 minutes

What letter comes two to the right of the letter which comes two letters below the letter that comes midway between the letters R and J?

A	B	C	D	E
F	G	H	I	J
K	L	M	N	O
P	Q	R	S	T
U	V	W	X	Y	Z

A Z
B Y
C T
D R

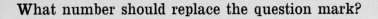

What number should replace the question mark?

1 4 13 40 121

?

A 243
B 221
C 364
D 390

What comes next?

triangle
square
pentagon
hexagon
?

A nonagon
B octagon
C polygon
D heptagon

On which target has 205 been scored?

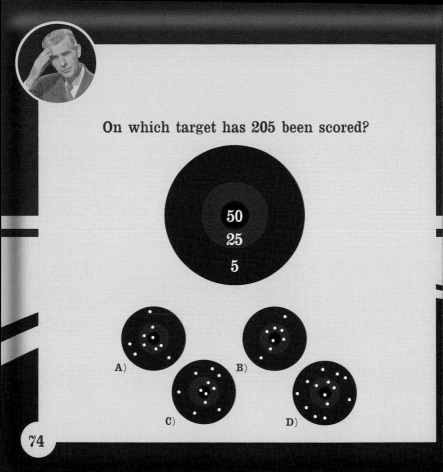

50

25

5

A)

B)

C)

D)

What comes next?

A C F H K ?

A O
B M
C N
D L

What number should replace the question mark?

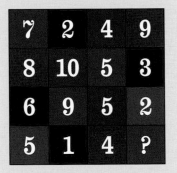

7	2	4	9
8	10	5	3
6	9	5	2
5	1	4	?

A 9
B 4
C 6
D 8

If
SHELL
is worth
77345
what is the value of
SHOE?

A 2368
B 3045
C 7703
D 5403

What single letter will convert the three
four-letter words below into
three five-letter words?

RAID
ROSE
MALE

A T
B P
C A
D B

Which is the missing tile?

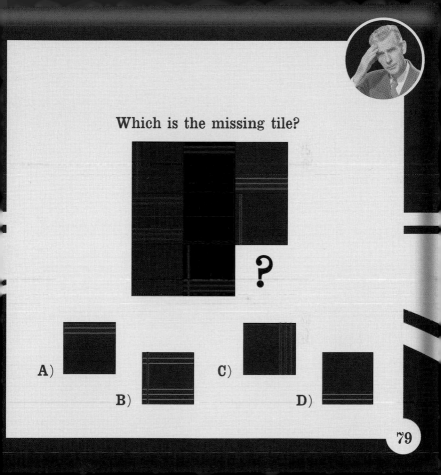

A)

B)

C)

D)

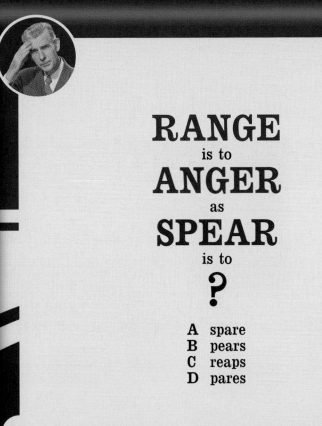

RANGE
is to
ANGER
as
SPEAR
is to
?

A spare
B pears
C reaps
D pares

How many is

twelve thousand twelve hundred and twelve?

A 121212
B 131212
C 13212
D 12112

What letter will complete a six-letter word reading clockwise?

A T
B F
C D
D G

82

What letter, when added to the
beginning of a word meaning

DISTANCE

or

LIMIT

produces

A TYPE OF FRUIT?

A   T
B   G
C   R
D   O

Which is the missing tile?

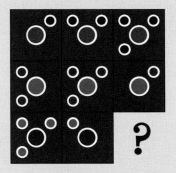

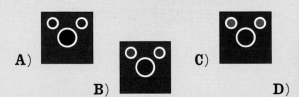

A)

B)

C)

D)

Only one group of six letters below can be rearranged to spell out a six-letter word in the English language.

A APUBNR

B EOPLTM

C APUHLE

D AINTLE

Can you find the word?

Which is the missing tile?

A)

B)

C)

D)

What number should replace the question mark?

101
100
97
92
85
?

A 78
B 77
C 75
D 76

Three of the four strings of letters below can
be combined to spell out a phrase.
Which is the unused string?

A aho
B ots
C inc
D art

What word completes the list below?

caravan
bejewel
bikinis
Solomon
?

A Romulus
B cabaret
C cumulus
D moronic

What number should replace the question mark?

A 5
B 9
C 1
D 7

90

What number comes next?

382 173 821 738

?

A 812
B 217
C 628
D 721

SOLUTIONS

Page 4: C 3: each number indicates how many numbers are in adjacent squares to it, either horizontally, vertically or diagonally.

Page 5: A The large ellipse alternates horizontal/vertical and the dot alternates blue/red.

Page 6: D Tree: the consonants TRLDP are being repeated in the same order.

Page 7: A APERM = remap.

Page 8: B Lines are carried forward to a pentagon from within the two pentagons immediately below it, except where two lines appear in the same position in both these pentagons, in which case they are canceled out.

Page 9: A 63: start at 1 and work clockwise jumping to alternate segments and adding 2, 4, 8, 16, 32.

Page 10: B 14: add the first and last numbers and then work inwards; each pair of numbers totals 21.

Page 11: D 2: each number indicates the number of triangles it is inside.

Page 12: A ESE.

Page 13: C 9: in each row multiply the first and last numbers, then reverse to get the number in the middle column. Thus 3 x 9 = 27 (or 72 when reversed).

Page 14: B $0.25.

Page 15: C KP: there are two interwoven sequences: ABcDefGhijK and ZYxWvuTsrqP.

Page 16: A L: ZyXwvUtsrQponmL.

Page 17: A ADY: the first three strings added to the last three strings spell finish, orator, steady.

Page 18: B Add both sides together to obtain three concentric circles.

92

SOLUTIONS

Page 19: C Success: each word commences with the fifth and fourth
letters, in that order, of the previous word.

Page 20: D Q: to spell headquarters.

Page 21: C Add lines working clockwise. Previous lines become broken at the stage
after they are added.

Page 22: D Looking at lines across skip one letter. Looking down skip two letters.

Page 23: C Mentor: each word contains the letters abc, def, ghi, jkl, mno respectively
in the correct order.

Page 24: D Lasses: when the columns are combined the words brokerage, prosecute,
daredevil and sunglasses appear.

Page 25: C The rest are exactly the same when rotated.

Page 26: B CIUTN = tunic.

Page 27: C Red and green are reversed. In all the other the diamond/circle overlap is
red and the circle/square overlap is green.

Page 28: C 10: it is the number of straight lines in the spelling of each word.

Page 29: D Speak last = pea stalks.

Page 30: C 14.

Page 31: A 3.

Page 32: A E.

Page 33: B All the others contain the same sequence of colors. In C orange and
purple are reversed.

Page 34: A In all the others the color of the outer ring repeats the color in the center.

Page 35: D MNOPQ: two letters, skip one, three letters, skip one, four letters, skip one,
five letters.

Page 36: B 0: looking across multiply the first and last numbers to obtain the number
formed by the middle two columns. Thus 5 x 6 = 30.

SOLUTIONS

Page 37: C ead: go it alone.
Page 38: D The rectangle and diamond change places and the top and bottom colors in the diamond change places.
Page 39: D 12: 6 x 8 ÷ 4 = 12.
Page 40: A So that each circle contains one heart, diamond, club and spade.
Page 41: B Club: all words in the left-hand column can be prefixed with night. All words in the right-hand column can be prefixed with day.
Page 42: B Tuesday.
Page 43: A GHKJ: the rest consist of four consecutive letters of the alphabet with the last two letters reversed.
Page 44: B Add a line to the bottom of the first and last figures and remove a line from the middle figure.
Page 45: B So that the total of numbers in each line of the triangle is 22.
Page 46: B G.
Page 47: D Each line repeats the same pattern of lines/color.
Page 48: C H: the words PULL/PUSH appear alternately PPUULSLH.
Page 49: A U: to spell urbane.
Page 50: C The circle without lines goes inside the circle with lines; and the lines transfer inside the circle.
Page 51: B Unbreakable.
Page 52: A LADS: MISS is being changed to LADY one letter at a time.
Page 53: A Fan: to produce rough diamond, heartache, spadework and fanclub.
Page 54: D 15: Opposite sides of a die total 7.
Page 55: B 4157: take the value of respective letters in the alphabet of each word i.e. D(4) O(15) G(7).

SOLUTIONS

Page 56: D.

Page 57: C JY: the first and last letters of November, December, January, February, March, April.

Page 58: C O: to produce; echo, foxtrot, golf, hotel (the Phonetic Alphabet)

Page 59: D nebular: each word starts with the first two letters of the planets in order from the sun; Mercury, Venus, Earth, Mars, Jupiter, Saturn, Uranus, Neptune.

Page 60: B At each stage the second disc moves to last.

Page 61: A L: place/pace.

Page 62: D The dot is in two circles only; in the rest it is in three circles.

Page 63: B 1: average = 6; second highest odd number = 7.

Page 64: A The red dot moves from corner to corner diagonally. The white circle moves clockwise by one corner at a time.

Page 65: C.

Page 66: D Rapper Ed = prepared.

Page 67: D Bland.

Page 68: A Looking across and down, only same color spots that appear in the same position in the first two squares are carried forward to the third square, however, they then change from yellow to red and vice versa.

Page 69: D SOX: PqrS, MnO, TuvwX.

Page 70: A 18 minutes.

Page 71: A Z.

Page 72: C 364: multiply by 3 and add 1 each time.

Page 73: D Heptagon.

Page 74: C.

Page 75: B M: AbCdeFgHijKlM.

SOLUTIONS

Page 76: D 8: in each row and column sets of alternate digits total the same.
Page 77: B 3045: the words appear when the numbers are punched into a calculator and it is then viewed upside down.
Page 78: B P: rapid, prose, maple.
Page 79: A Each row and column contains one line, two lines and three lines positioned left side, top and bottom.
Page 80: B Pears: move the first letter to last.
Page 81: C 13212.
Page 82: C D: to spell ordain.
Page 83: D O: range/orange.
Page 84: C Each row and column contains one/two/three top outer dots and each row contains the same color combinations.
Page 85: D AINTLE = entail.
Page 86: A Each row and column contains a large blue circle, a broad yellow left-hand stripe, a red right-hand side stripe, a top yellow stripe and a bottom blue stripe.
Page 87: D 76: subtract 1,3,5,7,9.
Page 88: D Art: in cahoots.
Page 89: C Cumulus: the words contain a, e, i, o, u in turn, repeated alternately.
Page 90: B 7: 199 + 648 - 847.
Page 91: A 217: the numbers 38217 are repeated in the same order.